TO DAD   LOVE   FROM SIMON ©

ANTMEN

CARRY AWAY

MY

THOUGHTS

AS

SOON AS   I

THINK

THEM

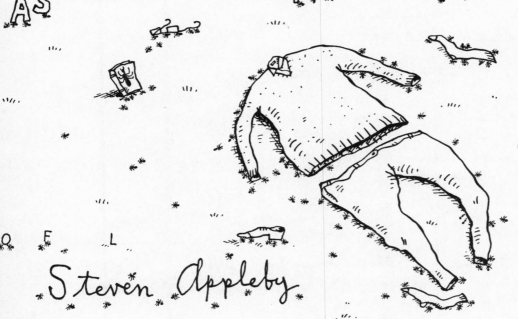

ANTMEN CARRY AWAY MY THOUGHTS AS SOON AS I THINK THEM.

OF L

Steven Appleby

First published in 1997
This paperback edition published 1998

The moral right of the author has been asserted

Bloomsbury Publishing PLC, 38 Soho Square,
London W1V 5DF

A CIP catalogue record for this book is
available from the British Library

10 9 8 7 6 5 4 3 2 1

ISBN 0 7475 3820 4

Printed in Great Britain by St Edmundsbury Press, Suffolk

Dear Reader,

Most of the drawings in this book first appeared in The Guardian — the remainder (pages 16, 59, 62, 63, 64 & 78) were published by The Sunday Telegraph.

I have re-drawn all the black and white drawings for the book in order to standardise the shapes and sizes of the drawings, and because they were originally coloured. The colour pages are exactly the pictures which appeared in the newspapers.

There was something else I wanted to say, but, er... um... ah...

Steven Appleby 7.9.97

London...

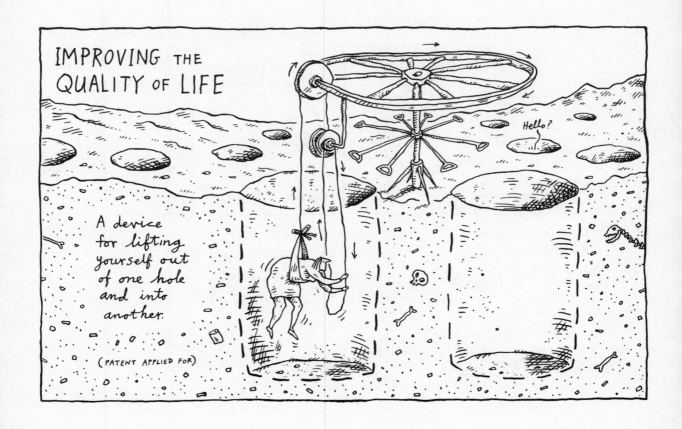

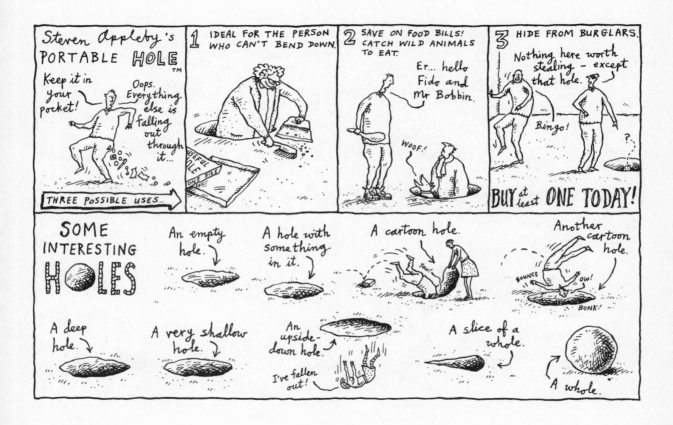

IMAGINING NOTHING

TRY THINKING OF:

i – A blank sheet of paper.

ii – A hole.

iii – The inside of a rubber ball.

iv – A cat's brain.

THINKING OF NOTHING IS IMPOSSIBLE, SINCE IF YOU CAN THINK OF A THING – EVEN IF IT'S NOTHING – THEN YOU MUST BE THINKING OF SOMETHING...

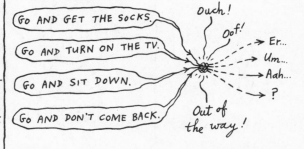

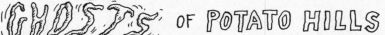
GHOSTS OF POTATO HILLS

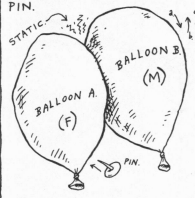

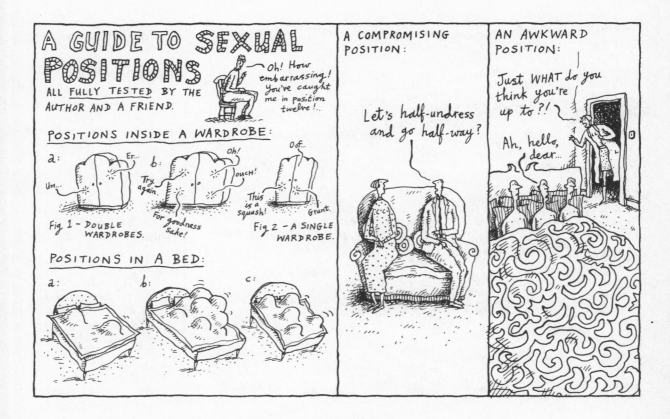

WHATEVER YOU DO, PLEASE DO NOT TOUCH!

MR SYLVESTER, THE BARTRAM FAMILY'S PET GOAT, HAS BEEN HEARD WHINNYING AT NIGHT IN HIS STY.

The conditions in here are disgraceful!

That sounds like WHINING, not WHINNYING.

THUD!

CRUNCH

Yow!

WHUMP!

YIP!

CLOUDS TOO HEAVY TO REMAIN IN THE SKY THUD TO THE GROUND NARROWLY MISSING PICNICKERS, DOGS AND CAMPER VANS.

A LOBSTER THE SIZE OF AN AIRPORT WALKS ABOUT ON PLYMOUTH.

SMASH!

CRASH

CRUSH

WHAM!

HELP!
HELP!

I found this knob, Mum, but I only turned it a tiny bit...

QUACK!
QUACK!

Honestly...

PLANET EARTH FACTORY SET DO NOT ADJUST

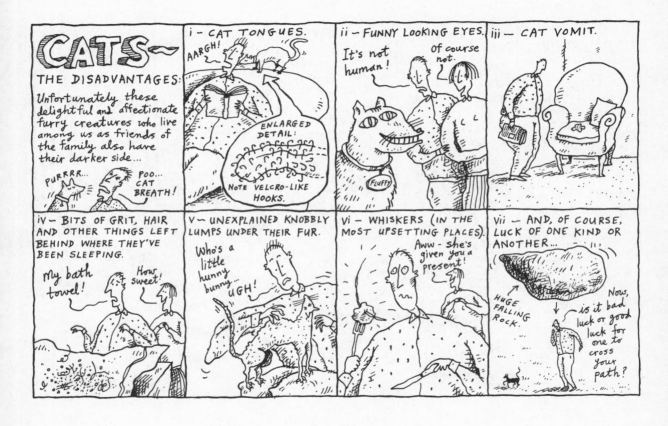

VIEWS INSIDE FISH, FROGS

and OTHER THINGS...

SOME PICTURESQUE CLOUD FORMATIONS SEEN INSIDE A PLAICE.

A LOVELY SUNSET WITHIN A HALIBUT.

A DELIGHTFUL MISTY MORNING INSIDE A FROG.

THE ENTIRE UNIVERSE - VISIBLE INSIDE A TURNIP IF YOU KNOW WHERE TO LOOK.

THE RATHER DISAPPOINTING CONTENTS OF A BALLOON.

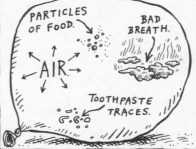

PARTICLES OF FOOD.

BAD BREATH.

AIR

TOOTHPASTE TRACES.

UNKNOWN INVENTORS Number 1 · DR. ROGER WINKEL.

Eureka!

Here's Roger Winkel wearing his everlasting force-field trousers. These never wear out because the invisible field keeps them from rubbing against buttocks, legs and chairs.

Comfy.

Here's Roger again modelling trousers, socks, shoes, coat, hat, gloves and underwear made from his unique force-field fabric.

Thanks to Roger, in the future people will need only one of each item of clothing as his material never needs cleaning — dust, dirt, stains and even smells are held away by the invisible rays.

MUD SLIPS OFF LEAVING FABRIC SPOTLESS

Washing the clothes would be a complete waste of time since water and soap powder can never physically touch them.

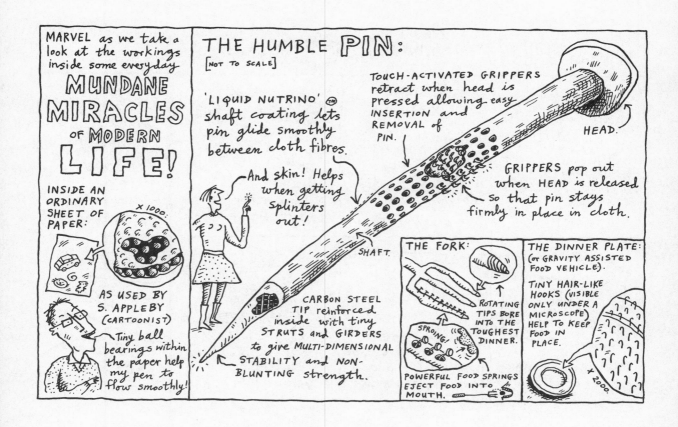

MARVEL as we take a look at the workings inside some everyday

MUNDANE MIRACLES OF MODERN LIFE!

INSIDE AN ORDINARY SHEET OF PAPER:

x 1000

AS USED BY S. APPLEBY (CARTOONIST)

Tiny ball bearings within the paper help my pen to flow smoothly!

THE HUMBLE PIN:

[NOT TO SCALE]

'LIQUID NUTRINO' ® shaft coating lets pin glide smoothly between cloth fibres.

And skin! Helps when getting splinters out!

SHAFT.

CARBON STEEL TIP reinforced inside with tiny STRUTS and GIRDERS to give MULTI-DIMENSIONAL STABILITY and NON-BLUNTING strength.

TOUCH-ACTIVATED GRIPPERS retract when head is pressed allowing easy INSERTION and REMOVAL of PIN.

HEAD.

GRIPPERS pop out when HEAD is released so that pin stays firmly in place in cloth.

THE FORK:

ROTATING TIPS BORE INTO THE TOUGHEST DINNER.

SPROING!

POWERFUL FOOD SPRINGS EJECT FOOD INTO MOUTH.

THE DINNER PLATE:
(or GRAVITY ASSISTED FOOD VEHICLE).

TINY HAIR-LIKE HOOKS (VISIBLE ONLY UNDER A MICROSCOPE) HELP TO KEEP FOOD IN PLACE.

x 2000

GRASPING THE UNIMAGINABLE

SOME HELPFUL WAYS TO THINK OF THE UNIVERSE...

A HANDLE.

A REFLECTION.

A SOCK THAT IS ALWAYS INSIDE-OUT.

A TANGLED BALL OF STRING.

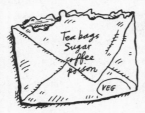

THE BACK OF AN ENVELOPE.

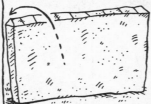

THE OTHER SIDE OF A HIGH WALL - ALONG WITH GREENER GRASS.

A VACUUM FLASK.

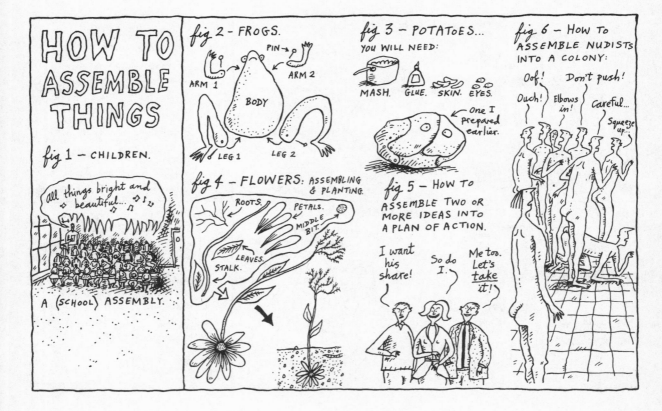

GARDENING TIPS — Why not try some of these ideas at home?

'Wicked Queen' variety apple tree (grows poisonous fruit).

Sun dial.

Gloomy. Bright. Hot.

Bottomless sand pit.

caterpillar.

caterwall.

Pruning Tip – glue the prunes on securely.

GLUE

RUMBLE

Water feature – a hot geyser imported from Iceland.

A topiary W.C.

A topiarist.

A NEW KIND OF GARDEN SEAT.

Comfy!

HOW TO SPOT
GOOD and BAD FRUIT and VEGETABLES

SELECTED BY
Steven Appleby.

A Virtuous Grape.

A Peerless Parsnip.

An Admirable Apple.

A Proper Prune.

An Unrivalled Artichoke.

A Laudable Cherry.

A Rare Pea.

An Upright Sprout.

A Splendid Carrot.

A Good-Hearted Banana.

An Evil Onion.

A Treacherous Potato.

A Vile Bean.

A Deceitful Satsuma.

A Malignant Melon.

A Two-Faced Pear.

A Left-handed Asparagus.

A Wicked Raddish.

A Baleful Plum.

LEARNING TO TALK 'VEGETABLE'...

BUILDING BRIDGES

Let's make up...

A STURDY BRIDGE BETWEEN TWO PEOPLE OF LIKE MINDS.

Good idea.   I agree.

AN UNINSPIRED YET FUNCTIONAL BRIDGE BETWEEN MR AND MRS BOBBIN.

A RATHER RICKETY BRIDGE BETWEEN A WOMAN AND HER EX-PARTNER.

Mummy!   Daddy!

A DELIGHTFUL BUT FLIMSY, IMPRACTICAL AND UN-THOUGHT-THROUGH BRIDGE BETWEEN TWO YOUNG THINGS.

I like spinach.   Me too! Let's get married...

A BRIDGE BETWEEN AN ESTRANGED MOTHER & SON.

Darling!   Aw, Mum...

CRASH!

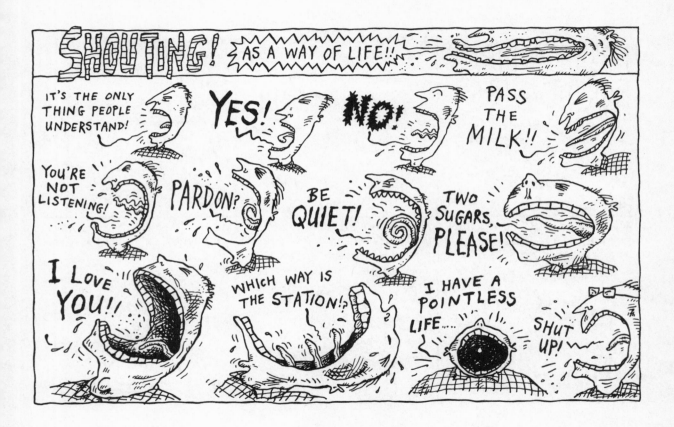

POINTED OUT AS A PUBLIC SERVICE!

Beware the abyss of embarrassment!

THE WORD 'PENETRATED' CAUSES A HUSH TO FALL AT MRS WOGGLER'S GARDEN EVENT.

SAYING 'PLEASE SIT DOWN' TO PEOPLE WITH NO BOTTOMS.

ALIEN SKIES

We live inside this planet – what is a sky?

THE SKY ON PLANET PERCY IS PARTICULARLY LOW.

BUMP!
ouch!

ON BUSTER 6 THE SKY IS DOWN BELOW AND THE GROUND UP ABOVE.

Walking the dog is tricky.

I'll just dig the garden... Aaagh!

THE SKY ON THIS GAS GIANT HAS TO BE SHORED UP TO STOP IT COLLAPSING UNDER THE IMMENSE GRAVITY.

CREAK...

ON THIS PLANET LIFE HAS EVOLVED IN THE SKY. THE GROUND IS UNINHABITABLE.

Don't eat with your mouth open, Byron!

PLANET PINKY HAS A SKY SO SOLID THAT PEOPLE FROM OUR WORLD CAN STAND ON TOP OF IT.

What's that rumbling?

A flock of birds flying under our feet.

Look. A cloud!

ROTOVATING THE CLOUDS

A HERD OF COWS supported by hot air balloons. The cows produce methane which fuels the burners.

PLANTING THUNDER CLOUD SEEDLINGS

HARVESTING NIMBUS CLOUDS.

FLOATING MARKET GARDENS orbit constantly to catch the sunlight 24 hours a day.

IN THE FUTURE, WHEN THE WORLD'S POPULATION HAS INCREASED UNTIL EVERY INCH OF LAND, SEA & SKY IS NEEDED TO GROW FOOD, SKY-FARMERS WILL PLOUGH, SOW & REAP THE SPECIAL CROPS DEVELOPED TO THRIVE IN THE INHOSPITABLE FIELDS OF THE CLOUDS.

PLOUGHING:

TYRES FILLED WITH HELIUM.

INSIDERS DISCOVER THAT THEY HAVE BEEN OUTSIDE ALL ALONG.

A USEFUL GUIDE TO SHOP LIFTING

The corner shop has gone!

Where can we go to buy corners now?

WRONG!
STRAIGHT LEGS, BENT BACK.

GRUNT...

RIGHT!
BENT LEGS, BACK STRAIGHT.

Clear off!

Let me have a go!

A LIGHT SHOP:

Edward's LIGHTBULBS

Hoi!!

Easy!

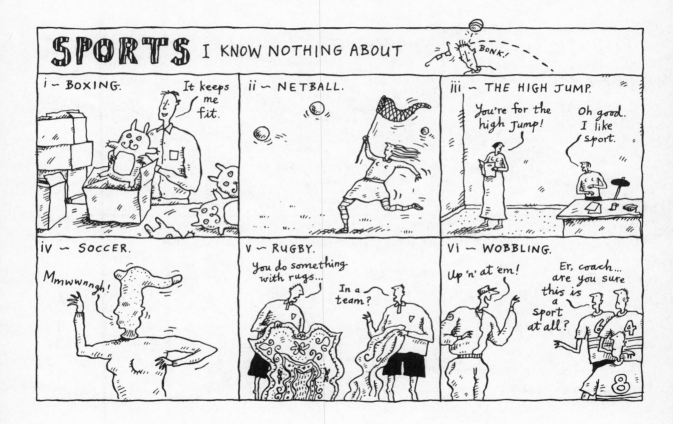

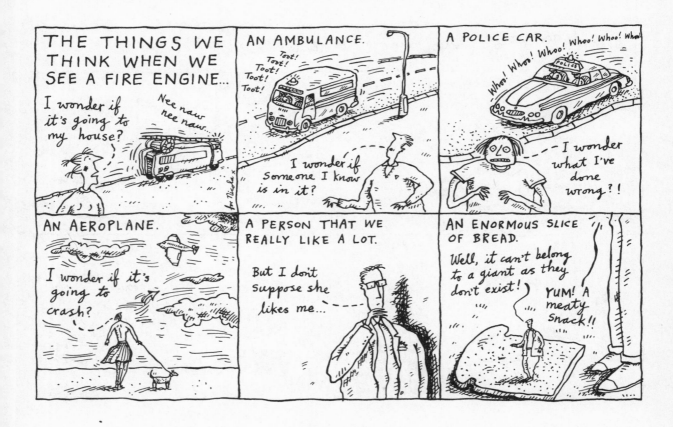

WHAT HAPPENS WHEN YOU DIE!

It's dusty in here...

SOME PEOPLE BELIEVE THERE'S A LIFE AFTER DEATH.

Oh no. Look who it is...

Hello.

Fancy meeting you here!

COMMONSENSE PEOPLE BELIEVE IN NOTHING.

Be practical!

DEAD PET.

CLUNK

RELIGIOUS FOLK PUT THEIR FAITH IN AN ALL-KNOWING GOD.

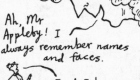

Ah, Mr Appleby! I always remember names and faces.

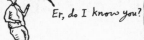

Er, do I know you?

OTHERS FIND COMFORT IN SOME KIND OF VAGUE, ER, INDEFINABLE, UM, SORT OF, WELL, NOT EXACTLY A SPIRIT...

I just have a feeling that this life isn't all there is...

SCIENTISTS TAKE A LOGICAL APPROACH.

We die, then bacteria break the body down into sludge and I guess the soul too.

YOUNG PEOPLE BELIEVE DEATH WON'T HAPPEN TO THEM.

I don't even have any wrinkles!

FAST

Toot! Toot!

LEAP

IN FACT I CAN REVEAL THAT WE ALL LIVE ON THROUGH OUR 'THINGS'— SUCH AS PULLOVERS, SOCKS, SHOES AND CUTLERY.

Dad?

HIS SWEATER.

Yes, it's me, son!

WHAT HAPPENS WHEN **YOU** DIE...

i – NOTHING.

Excuse me, is Heaven this way, or...

No such place, mate.

ii – ALL YOUR ACCUMULATED KNOWLEDGE AND EXPERIENCE IS LOST.

So none of us knows that clever little short cut to the Saver Centre?

I wish we'd asked him before it was too late.

iii – ALL YOUR THINGS ARE DIVIDED UP.

Do you want his collection of price tags?

Bin them.

CHARITY SHOP Collection

iv – SO WHY NOT SET FIRE TO YOUR BELONGINGS, SELL YOUR HOUSE AND LIVE SIMPLY IN A MOTOR HOME?

He was burning his belongings and died in the inferno.

Sad....ish.

TELEPHONING the DEAD
Well, I don't believe it's possible to telephone the dead.
Trying to connect you...
Hello? Mum?
Sorry. I'm afraid you've got the wrong number.
This number has been changed...
I'll just put you on hold...
Ave maria...
I'll try and transfer you...
Oh you'll never go to heaven... etc...
This call is being diverted...
Hello. You've reached your mother's voicemail...
BEEP
BEEP
BEEP
BEEP...
You were right.

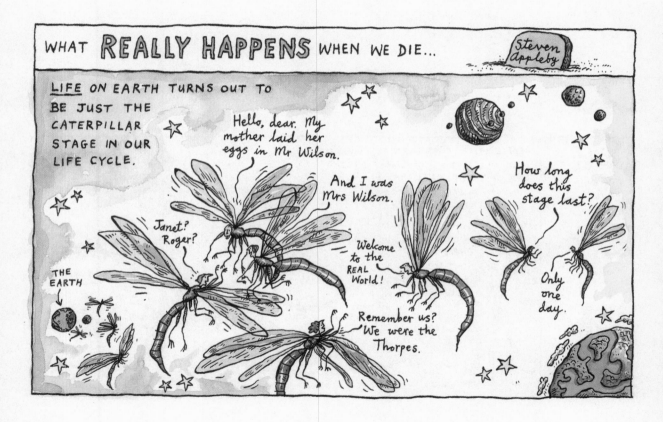

MONSTERLAND!
by Steven Appleby.
Alfie learns that the monster has 12 stomachs, each specialising in digesting a particular bit of him.
YUM! MY FAVOURITE!
Disgusting.
SLAVER
HEADS & BRAINS
KNEES
STRING
TEETH
SWORDS & SCABBARDS
PACKED LUNCH (including tin).
MARBLES
SHOES & SOCKS
BALLOONS
ODD BITS OF LEGO
BONES & OTHER CRUNCHY PARTS
EVERYTHING ELSE...

HAVING A CHILD MAKES YOU REALISE...
a Steven appleby announcement TM
... HOW SHORT A CHILD IS.
So tiny!
Da!
... HOW SHORT CHILDHOOD IS.
Got any condoms I can borrow, Dad?
SKUNK
... HOW SHORT YOU ARE.
Yo, Dad!
I'M IN A BAND
PENSION
... HOW SHORT LIFE IS.
Hi Dad! We brought the kids to your deathbed. They're so TINY!

THE AMAZING WAY OSMOSIS WORKS...
I've got a terrible headache...
Perhaps it will leave my head and go into this chest of drawers by osmosis.
Nope – I've still got the headache.
EMPTY!

3 WAYS TO TRIP UP A POLITICIAN...

Steven Appleby THANKS K.

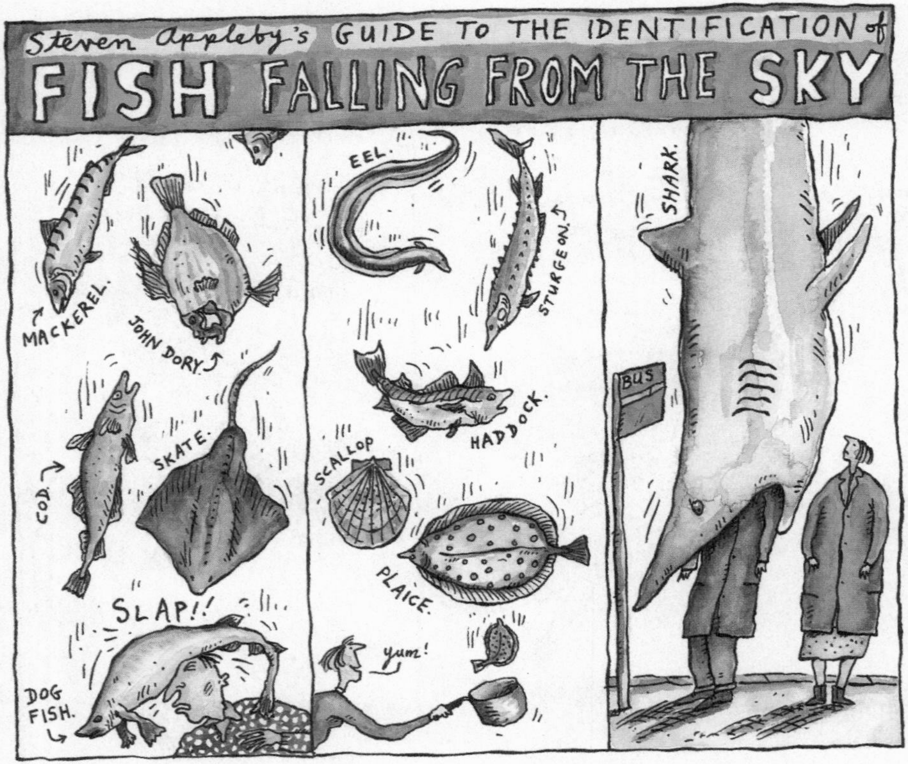

Steven Appleby's GUIDE TO THE IDENTIFICATION of FISH FALLING FROM THE SKY

MACKEREL.

JOHN DORY.

COD.

SKATE.

SLAP!!

DOG FISH.

EEL.

STURGEON.

HADDOCK.

SCALLOP

PLAICE.

yum!

SHARK.

BUS

PERVY PEOPLE!

studied by
MR STEVEN APPLEBY

Oops! Ha ha! You've caught me out! Just doing some research...

Ready, darling! Oh...

A TOPLESS WOMAN.

A KINKY MAN.

It's hard to find a partner with kinks in all the same places!

A PIERCED COUPLE.

We've never regretted it!

A TATTOOED FAMILY.

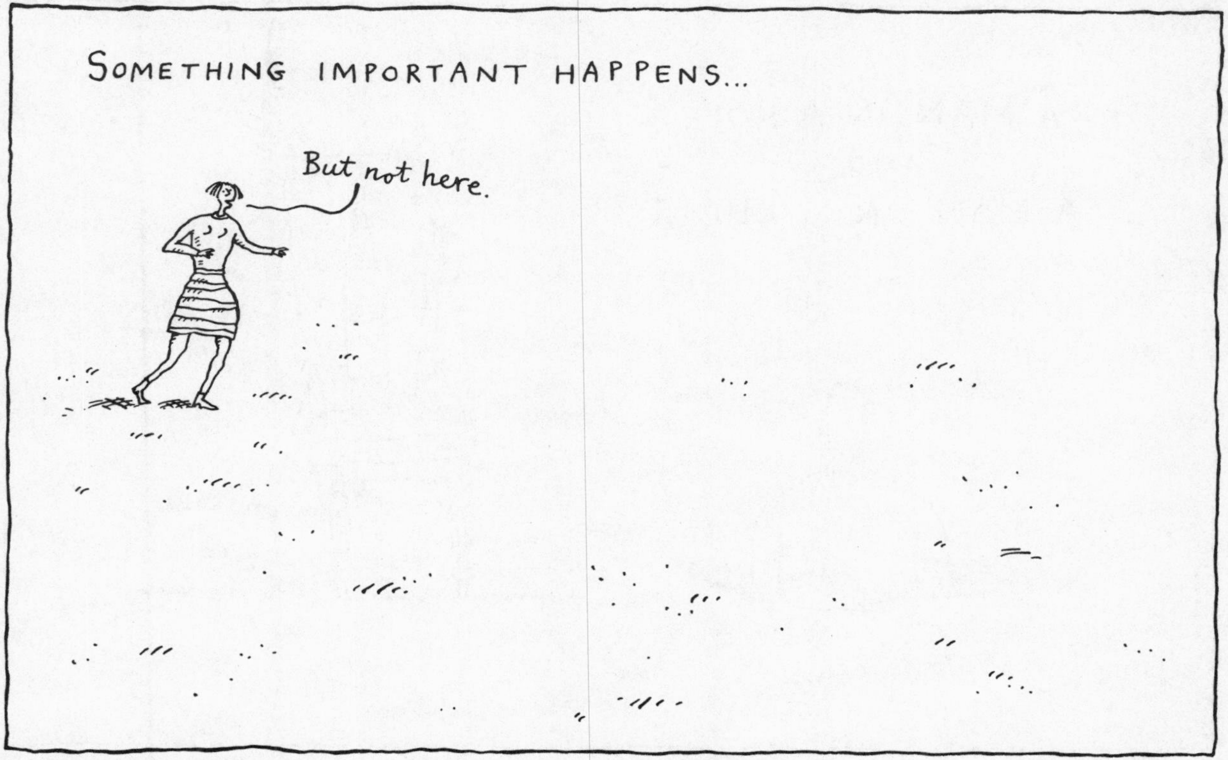
SOMETHING IMPORTANT HAPPENS...
But not here.

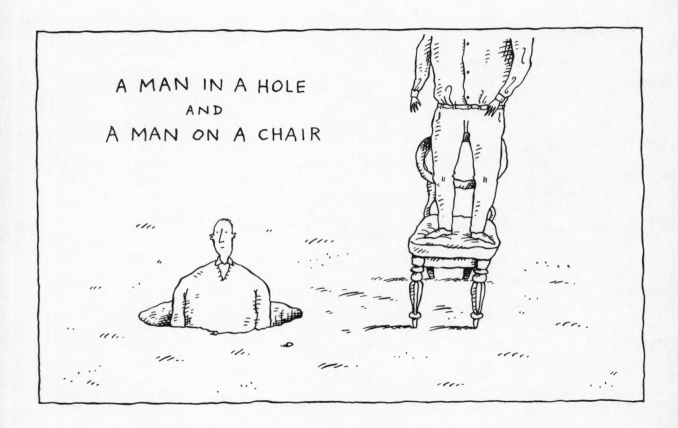

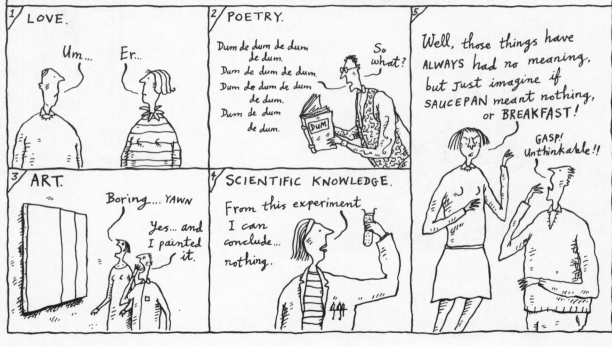

PERHAPS THIS FRUITBOWL IS A
METAPHOR FOR LIFE AND DEATH?

DOES THIS FALLING TEAPOT
SIGNIFY SOMETHING
IMPORTANT?

THESE THREE DOGS DON'T
REPRESENT ANYTHING AT ALL.

THIS
TITLE BOX
IS IN THE WRONG PLACE.

Could there be
some deep
significance
to it??

A DEATH ROBOT FROM PLANET
47c HELPS A SICK BUNNY
RABBIT — WHICH MUST
SYMBOLISE AN ETERNAL TRUTH.

HOWEVER, THE UNIVERSAL
FISHERMAN — WAITING FOREVER
AS THE TROUT OF INDECISION
CIRCLES THE HOOK OF DESTINY —
IS OBVIOUSLY UTTER RUBBISH!

Some strange and MEANINGLESS SHAPES

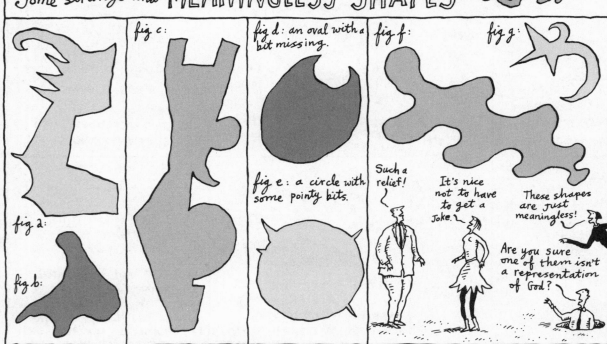

fig a:

fig b:

fig c:

fig d: an oval with a bit missing.

fig e: a circle with some pointy bits.

fig f:

fig g:

Such a relief!

It's nice not to have to get a joke.

These shapes are just meaningless!

Are you sure one of them isn't a representation of God?

UNKNOWN INVENTORS
Number 2
THE INVENTOR WHO GAVE UP AFTER THE 'YO'.
Well, it goes down alright...
TOTALLY STATIONARY

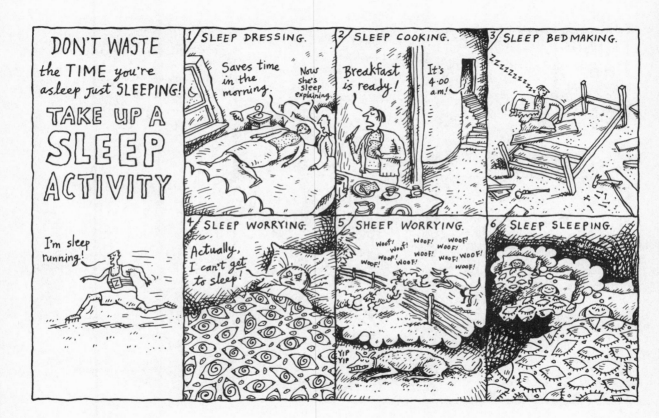

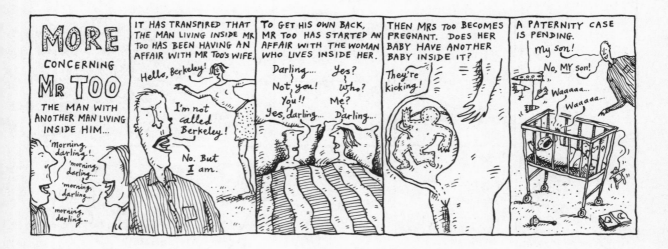

What WORTHLESS, POINTLESS & ANNOYING lives FLIES lead!

THESE ARE THE THINGS FLIES SPEND THEIR TIME DOING:

FLYING POINTLESS, CIRCULAR FLIGHTS BACK TO WHERE THEY STARTED FROM.

A CHIP.

RUBBING THEIR FRONT LEGS TOGETHER.

SITTING ON FOOD.

WALKING UPSIDE DOWN.

WALKING THE RIGHT WAY UP.

CIRCLING THE LIGHT BULB.

AND THEY NEVER LEARN! EITHER BY EXPERIENCE OR ANY OTHER WAY.

> Thousands of my pals have stuck to that strip of paper and died. I'll land on it and take a look...

FLIES DON'T UNDERSTAND PLAIN ENGLISH!

> GO AWAY!!

AND THEY DON'T LISTEN!!

> If you don't go away I will beat you to death!

WHY HAVE THEY BEEN BLESSED WITH THE ABILITY TO LOOK BACKWARDS? WHAT CONSTRUCTIVE USE DO THEY PUT IT TO?

> If I had fly eyes I'd invent the 360° Surround Vision T.V. set!

LET'S TAKE A LOOK AT ONE OF THESE UNFULFILLED CREATURES CLOSE UP:

FOOD & DUNG

FLY → PAPER

> I can't put it down!

UNKNOWN INVENTORS number 3

AN INVERTED SNOB

THIS MAN HAS INVENTED A NEW MOOD AND IS SUFFERING FROM IT.

I'm not an inventor! I'm an ARTIST!!

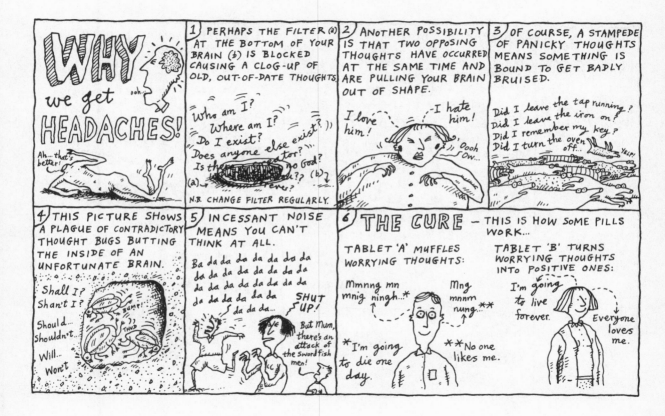

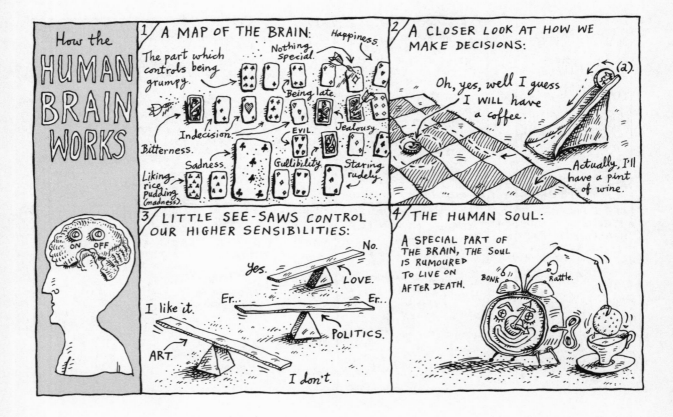

MR BOBBIN IS AN ISLAND...

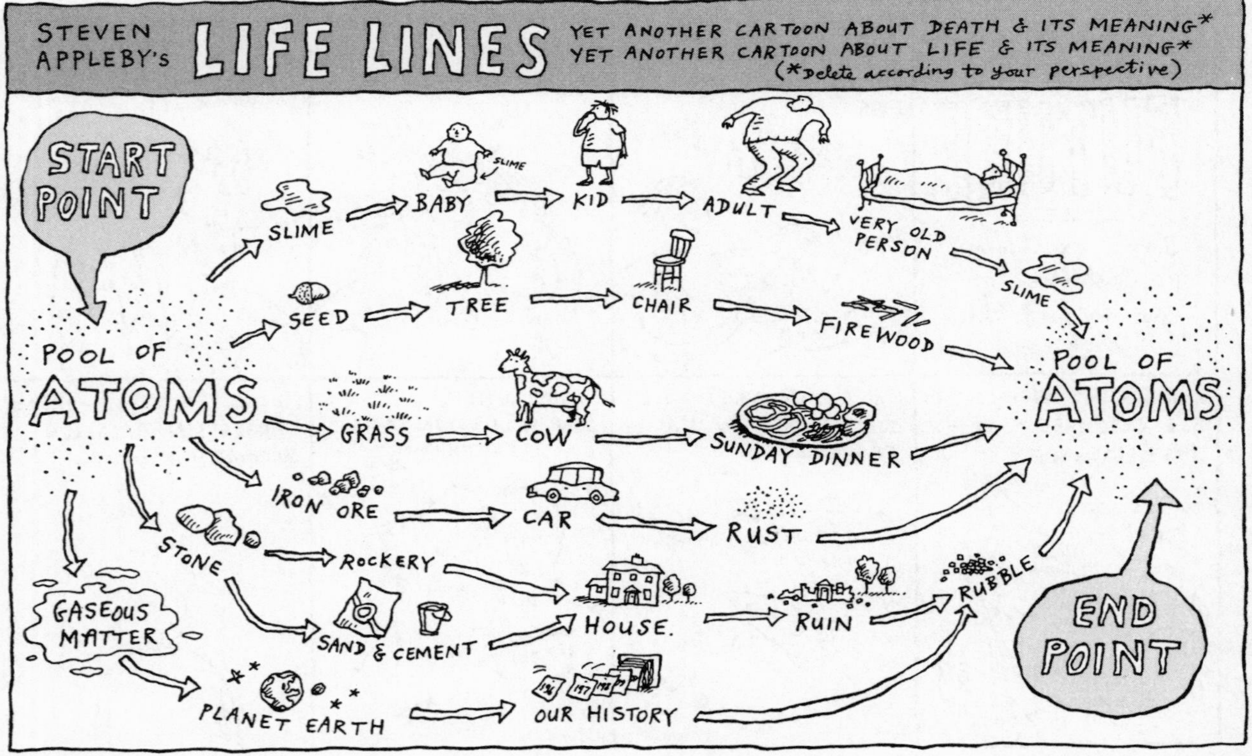
STEVEN APPLEBY'S
LIFE LINES
YET ANOTHER CARTOON ABOUT DEATH & ITS MEANING*
YET ANOTHER CARTOON ABOUT LIFE & ITS MEANING*
(*Delete according to your perspective)
START POINT
POOL OF ATOMS
SLIME
BABY
SLIME
KID
ADULT
VERY OLD PERSON
SLIME
SEED
TREE
CHAIR
FIREWOOD
GRASS
COW
SUNDAY DINNER
IRON ORE
CAR
RUST
STONE
ROCKERY
HOUSE.
RUIN
RUBBLE
SAND & CEMENT
GASEOUS MATTER
PLANET EARTH
OUR HISTORY
POOL OF ATOMS
END POINT

Some useful information concerning
the drawings in this book.

INCREDIBLE BUT TRUE!

IT CAN NOW BE REVEALED THAT THE CHARACTERS IN THIS BOOK COME COMPLETE WITH **REAL BODILY FUNCTIONS!**

STOCK FEMALE CHARACTER:

Oops... I've just broken wind!

Poo!

TOOT!

STOCK MALE CHARACTER:

Well, I've got B.O., dandruff and I pick my nose.

I CERTAINLY won't be in another drawing with you!

UGH.

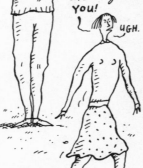

POORLY DRAWN CAT:

I've got bad breath – just like a flesh and blood cat.

NOW, THIS IS A CHARACTER WORTH... OH. HE'S GONE OFF TO USE THE LAVATORY!

Excuse me!

A QUALITY CONTROL PLEDGE!

1 – STEVEN APPLEBY CARTOONS CONTAIN ONLY THE VERY BEST QUALITY CHARACTERS:

FUNNY & INTERESTING CHARACTER.

Woof! Woof!

Oh... er... um... Yow!

INARTICULATE CHARACTER.

REJECT!

2 – THEY ARE GUARANTEED FREE OF OBSCURE AND MEANINGLESS PUNCHLINES...

A hinged walrus! Ha ha...

Ho ho! How pertinent. So true.

Spot on! Hee hee...

ONLY GRADE ONE CARTOON INKS & COLOURS ARE USED.

PLEASE NOTE:
OPINIONS EXPRESSED BY THE CHARACTERS ARE <u>NOT</u> NECESSARILY THOSE OF THE CREATOR!

S. Appleby stinks!

He's just not funny.

AND HERE IS YOUR

FREE GIFT!

A LONGER FUTURE

Just cut out these EXTRA LONG and UNBROKEN Life Lines and GLUE onto your palms. Now start planning your **100th** birthday party!

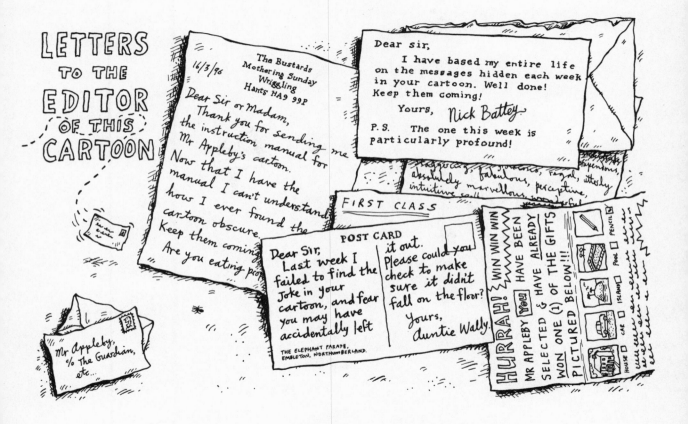